GARFIELD

Classics

Volume Six

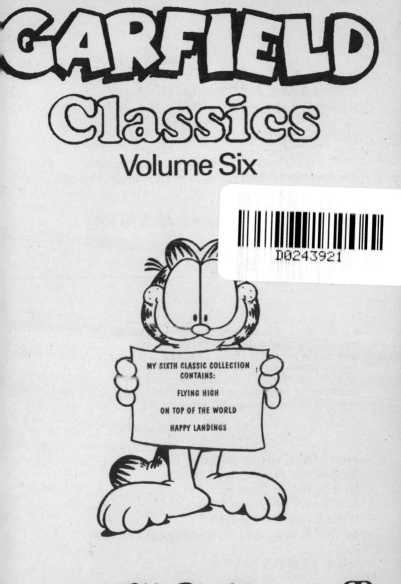

MY SIXTH CLASSIC COLLECTION
CONTAINS:

FLYING HIGH

ON TOP OF THE WORLD

HAPPY LANDINGS

JiM DAViS

First published by Ravette Publishing 2000
Reprinted 2001, 2003

Printed and bound in Great Britain
for Ravette Publishing Limited,
Unit 3, Tristar Centre,
Star Road, Partridge Green,
West Sussex RH13 8RA
by Cox & Wyman Ltd, Reading, Berkshire

ISBN: 1 84161 023 2

Garfield
Flying High

JIM DAVIS

© 1987 United Feature Syndicate, Inc.

© 1987 United Feature Syndicate, Inc.

JIM DAVIS 5-14

© 1987 United Feature Syndicate, Inc.

© 1987 United Feature Syndicate, Inc.

© 1987 United Feature Syndicate, Inc.

© 1987 United Feature Syndicate, Inc.

© 1987 United Feature Syndicate, Inc.

© 1987 United Feature Syndicate, Inc.

© 1987 United Feature Syndicate, Inc.

© 1987 United Feature Syndicate, Inc.

© 1987 United Feature Syndicate, Inc.

WHAT DOES ONE
HAVE TO DO TO GET
ONE'S BELLY SCRATCHED
AROUND HERE?

JIM DAVIS   8-11

© 1987 United Feature Syndicate, Inc.

© 1987 United Feature Syndicate, Inc.

© 1987 United Feature Syndicate, Inc.

JIM DAVIS

10-5

© 1987 United Feature Syndicate, Inc.

9-14

JIM DAVIS

© 1987 United Feature Syndicate, Inc.

JIM DAVIS 11-4

JIM DAVIS 11-25

© 1987 United Feature Syndicate, Inc.

TOO MUCH COFFEE, GARFIELD?

© 1987 United Feature Syndicate, Inc.

© 1987 United Feature Syndicate, Inc.

OH, NO! WHAT HAPPENED TO MY TOES?!

© 1987 United Feature Syndicate, Inc.

JIM DAVIS 1-1-88

© 1988 United Feature Syndicate, Inc.

© 1988 United Feature Syndicate, Inc.

© 1988 United Feature Syndicate, Inc.

© 1988 United Feature Syndicate, Inc.

SO, WHAT'S YOUR PROBLEM, GUYS?

© 1988 United Feature Syndicate, Inc.

WE DEMAND SEPARATE CLOSETS!

JIM DAVIS 2-18

2-23   JPM DAVIS

THAT'S MY PIE, GARFIELD, SO **HANDS OFF!**

© 1988 United Feature Syndicate, Inc.

JIM DAVIS

PLOOT

NNNGH!

JIM DAVIS

3-8

© 1988 United Feature Syndicate, Inc.

Garfield

Happy Landings

JiM DAViS

© 1988 United Feature Syndicate, inc.

© 1988 United Feature Syndicate, Inc.

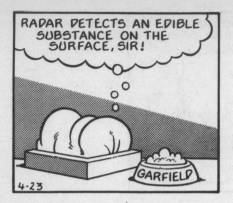

© 1988 United Feature Syndicate, Inc.

© 1988 United Feature Syndicate, Inc.

© 1988 United Feature Syndicate, Inc.

© 1988 United Feature Syndicate, Inc.

© 1988 United Feature Syndicate, Inc.

I CAN SEE TODAY IS GOING TO BE A REAL YAWN A MINUTE

JIM DAVIS 5-14

© 1988 United Feature Syndicate, Inc.

© 1988 United Feature Syndicate, Inc.

I'VE HEARD OF TOUGH GOLF COURSES...

© 1981 United Feature Syndicate, Inc.

BUT QUICKSAND TRAPS?

© 1988 United Feature Syndicate, Inc.

© 1988 United Feature Syndicate, Inc.

© 1988 United Feature Syndicate, Inc.

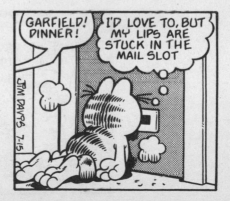

© 1988 United Feature Syndicate, Inc.

JiM DAViS 7-22

© 1988 United Feature Syndicate, Inc.

© 1988 United Feature Syndicate, Inc.

GARFIELD, YOUR SNORING KEPT ME UP HALF THE NIGHT

YOU DIDN'T STOP UNTIL SIX A.M.

I KNOW

© 1988 United Feature Syndicate, Inc.

THAT'S WHEN I INHALED MY BLANKET

JIM DAVIS

8-16

OTHER GARFIELD BOOKS AVAILABLE

Pocket Books	Price	ISBN
Bon Appetit	£3.50	1 84161 038 0
Byte Me	£3.50	1 84161 009 7
Double Trouble	£3.50	1 84161 008 9
Eat My Dust	£3.50	1 84161 098 4
Fun in the Sun	£3.50	1 84161 097 6
The Gladiator	£3.50	1 85304 941 7
Gooooooal!	£3.50	1 84161 037 2
Great Impressions	£3.50	1 85304 191 2
In Training	£3.50	1 85304 785 6
The Irresistible	£3.50	1 85304 940 9
Let's Party	£3.50	1 85304 906 9
Light Of My Life	£3.50	1 85304 353 2
On The Right Track	£3.50	1 85304 907 7
Pick Of The Bunch	£2.99	1 85304 258 7
Says It With Flowers	£2.99	1 85304 316 8
Shove At First Sight	£3.50	1 85304 990 5
To Eat, Or Not To Eat?	£3.50	1 85304 991 3
Wave Rebel	£3.50	1 85304 317 6
With Love From Me To You	£3.50	1 85304 392 3

new titles now available

No. 45 – Pop Star	£3.50	1 84161 151 4
No. 46 – Below Par	£3.50	1 84161 152 2

Theme Books		
Guide to Behaving Badly	£4.50	1 85304 892 5
Guide to Cat Napping	£4.50	1 84161 087 9
Guide to Coffee Mornings	£4.50	1 84161 086 0
Guide to Creatures Great & Small	£3.99	1 85304 998 0
Guide to Healthy Living	£3.99	1 85304 972 7
Guide to Pigging Out	£4.50	1 85304 893 3
Guide to Romance	£3.99	1 85304 894 1
Guide to The Seasons	£3.99	1 85304 999 9
Guide to Successful Living	£3.99	1 85304 973 5

2-in-1 Theme Books		
The Gruesome Twosome	£6.99	1 84161 143 3
Out For The Couch	£6.99	1 84161 144 1

Classics	Price	ISBN
Volume One	£5.99	1 85304 970 0
Volume Two	£5.99	1 85304 971 9
Volume Three	£5.99	1 85304 996 4
Volume Four	£5.99	1 85304 997 2
Volume Five	£5.99	1 84161 022 4
Volume Seven	£5.99	1 84161 088 7
Volume Eight	£5.99	1 84161 089 5
Volume Nine	£5.99	1 84161 149 2
Volume Ten	£5.99	1 84161 150 6

Little Books		
Food 'n' Fitness	£2.50	1 84161 145 X
Laughs	£2.50	1 84161 146 8
Love 'n' Stuff	£2.50	1 84161 147 6
Wit 'n' Wisdom	£2.50	1 84161 148 4

Miscellaneous
new title available June 2003

25 Years of Me!	£7.99	1 84161 173 5
Treasury 3	£9.99	1 84161 142 5
Treasury 2	£9.99	1 84161 042 9
Address Book (indexed) inc vat	£4.99	1 85304 904 2
21st Birthday Celebration Book	£9.99	1 85304 995 6

All Garfield books are available at your local bookshop or from the publisher at the address below. Just tick the titles required and send the form with your payment to:-

RAVETTE PUBLISHING
Unit 3, Tristar Centre, Star Road, Partridge Green, West Sussex RH13 8RA

Prices and availability are subject to change without notice.
Please enclose a cheque or postal order made payable to **Ravette Publishing** to the value of the cover price of the book and allow the following for UK postage and packing:

60P for the first book + 30p for each additional book
except *Garfield Treasuries* and *21st Birthday Celebration Book* . . . when please add £3.00 per copy for p&p

Name ....

Address ....

....

....